KW-487-001

OXFORD
UNIVERSITY PRESS

Shopping for a Party

Luther Reimer

We are going shopping for a party.

We need one cake and two videos.

We have to get **three** bags of crisps.

We have to get **four** pizzas, too.

Get some tomatoes.

We need **five** tomatoes.

We have too many sausages.

We need **six** sausages.

We need **seven** ice creams.

Get some hats too – eight hats.

Get some plates.

We need **nine** plates.

We have too many balloons.

We only need ten.

Now we can have a party!